3

EXCLUSIVE DISTRIBUTORS:
MUSIC SALES LIMITED, 14-15 BERNERS STREET, LONDON W1T 3LJ, UK.
WWW.MUSICSALES.COM
PRINTED IN THE EU.
AM999768

ISBN 978-1-84938-444-5

ABRSM

Music Theory Practice Papers 2018

ABRSM Grade 1

Music Theory Practice Papers 2018

ABRSM's *Music Theory Practice Papers 2018* are based on the 2018 Music Theory exam papers. The questions are the same as those used in recent exams.

Find out more about our Music Theory exams at **www.abrsm.org/theory**.

© 2018 by The Associated Board of the Royal Schools of Music
Published by ABRSM (Publishing) Ltd, a wholly owned subsidiary of ABRSM
Cover by Kate Benjamin & Andy Potts
Printed in England by Halstan & Co. Ltd, Amersham, Bucks., on materials from sustainable sources